USDIN ★ HAYES ★ NALTY

THE
AVANT-GUARDS™

VOLUME ONE

BOOM!
BOX™

BOOM! BOX™

THE AVANT-GUARDS Volume One Discover Now Edition, May 2019. Published by BOOM! Box, a division of Boom Entertainment, Inc. The Avant-Guards is ™ & © 2019 Scheme Machine Studios, LLC. Originally published in single magazine form as THE AVANT-GUARDS No. 1-4. ™ & © 2019 Scheme Machine Studios, LLC. All rights reserved. BOOM! Box™ and the BOOM! Box logo are trademarks of Boom Entertainment, Inc., registered in various countries and categories. All characters, events, and institutions depicted herein are fictional. Any similarity between any of the names, characters, persons, events, and/or institutions in this publication to actual names, characters, and persons, whether living or dead, events, and/or institutions is unintended and purely coincidental. BOOM! Box does not read or accept unsolicited submissions of ideas, stories, or artwork.

For information regarding the CPSIA on this printed material, call: (203) 595-3636 and provide reference #RICH – 844873.

BOOM! Studios, 5670 Wilshire Boulevard, Suite 400, Los Angeles, CA 90036-5679. Printed in USA. First Printing.

ISBN: 978-1-68415-355-8

CREATED & WRITTEN BY
CARLY USDIN

ILLUSTRATED BY
NOAH HAYES

COLORED BY
REBECCA NALTY

LETTERED BY
ED DUKESHIRE

COVER BY
VERONICA FISH

SERIES DESIGNER
GRACE PARK

COLLECTION DESIGNER
JILLIAN CRAB

EDITOR
SOPHIE PHILIPS-ROBERTS

SENIOR EDITOR
SHANNON WATTERS

NAME?

BRAVO. CHARLIE BRAVO.

HA!

TRANSF

≋KCHTK≋ ROGER THAT. 10-4.

YEAH... NEVER HEARD THAT ONE BEFORE.

EMBRACE THE
PYRAMID

GYM HOURS

LIFT
WITH
A
PAL

Y'ALL REMEMBER CHARLIE, RIGHT?

HI, CHARLIE!

COME, SIT.

YOU SHOULDN'T MESS AROUND WITH THAT, LIV.

THE LAST TIME OUR MOVEMENT CLASS HAD A HOMEWORK ASSIGNMENT THREE PEOPLE WOUND UP ON CRUTCHES.

O, THE AGONY OF DE-FEET!

HA

OH MY GOD, YOU ARE OUT OF CONTROL.

HA HA HA HA

HA HA HA

DID YOU GET THAT JOKE FROM A POPSICLE STICK?

SO, CHARLIE, WHY DON'T YOU TELL US A LITTLE ABOUT YOURSELF?

AND THEN WE CAN GO AROUND THE TABLE SO YOU CAN GET TO KNOW EVERYONE.

OH, WOW, WE'RE DOING THIS?

LIV LOVES ICE-BREAKERS.

SHE PRACTICALLY WROTE THE BOOK ON ICEBREAKERS.

SHE *LITERALLY* WROTE THE BOOK.

IT WAS A HIGH SCHOOL PROJECT *AND* A NEW YORK TIMES BESTSELLER!

BREAK THE ICE

OLIVIA BATES

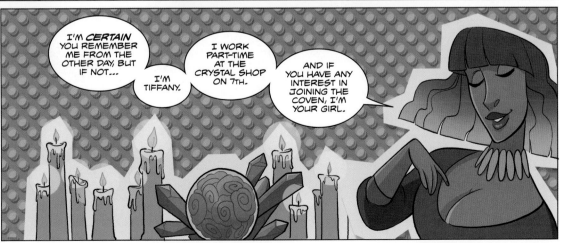

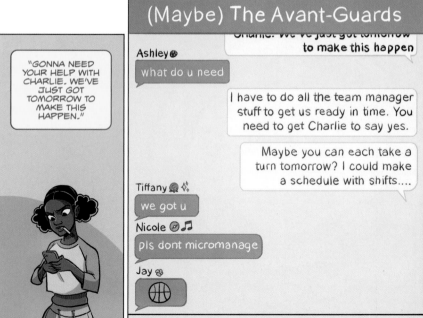

AFTER CLASS...

CHARLIE—
LET'S BALL!!
—JAY

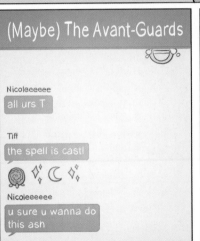

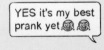

SO... UH... WHERE'S LIV?

SHE STRIKES ME AS A VERY PUNCTUAL PERSON.

OH, SHE IS.

HER PUNCTUALITY IS MATCHED ONLY BY HER FLAIR FOR THE DRAMATIC.

IS THAT THE CHICAGO BULLS WARM-UP MUSIC?

YES, BY THE ALAN PARSONS PROJECT.

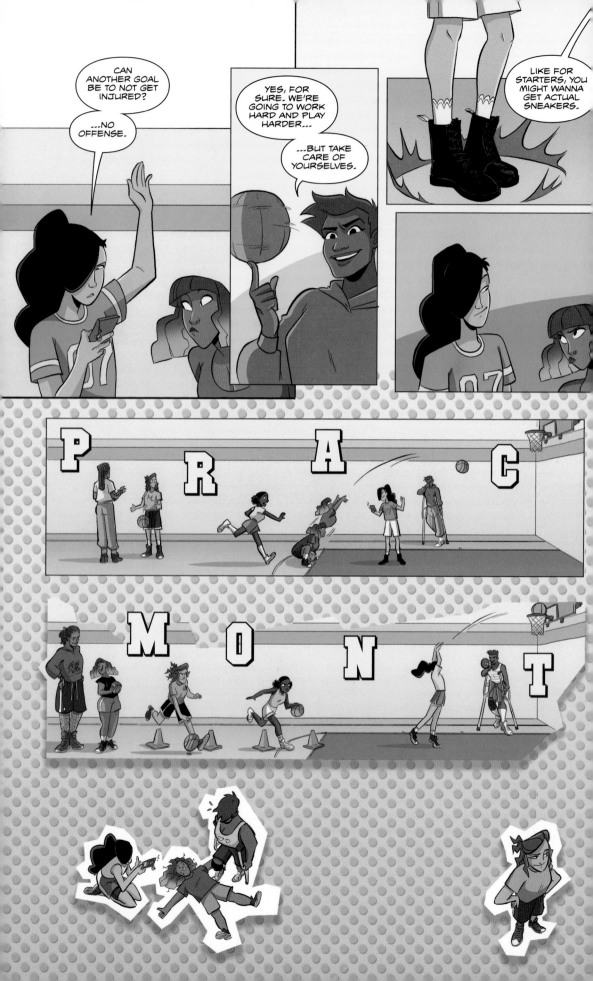

LIV, I CAN'T BELIEVE YOU GOT US THESE CUSTOM TRACK SUITS IN TIME FOR THE FIRST GAME.

I KNOW A GUY.

COME ON, CHARLIE. IT'S JUST A VAN.

KINDA LIKE A CAR...BUT BIGGER.

OK LIV, THIS IS IT, THE MOMENT YOU'VE BEEN WAITING FOR, PREPARING FOR, WORKING FOR. IT'S ALL HAPPENING!

I MEAN...WE'VE ONLY HAD ONE PRACTICE. WE'VE GOT NO PLAYS AND NO SUBS. BUT IT'S FINE. TOTALLY FINE.

WE'VE GOT JERSEYS AND TRACK SUITS THOUGH! GOTTA LOOK THE PART. FAKE IT 'TIL YOU MAKE IT, RIGHT?

AND WE'VE GOT HER. I HOPE I DIDN'T PUSH HER TOO HARD. SHE NORMALLY SEEMS SO TOUGH, BUT NOT RIGHT NOW. WAIT, IS SHE OK? I SHOULD SEE IF SHE'S OK.

HEY, UH...YOU OK?

MMHM.

I DON'T BELIEVE HER.

YOU KNOW, I GET REALLY NERVOUS BEFORE I GO ON STAGE. BUT I DO THESE VISUALIZATION EXERCISES AND THAT HELPS T--

IT'S NOT NERVES. OR, I MEAN, IT'S NOT *JUST* NERVES.

IT'S ANXIETY. I HAVEN'T PLAYED A GAME IN A MINUTE.

I USED TO GET PANIC ATTACKS ON THE BUS TO AWAY GAMES. I THINK THE VAN IS JUST BRINGING A LOT OF THOSE FEELINGS BACK.

WOW, CHARLIE. I DIDN'T REALIZE...

THAT SOUNDS REALLY OVERWHELMING AND SCARY.

DID YOU PLAY AT STATE?

MOMENTS LATER...

CAN I HAVE BOTH TEAMS OVER HERE PLEASE?

NORMALLY WE JUST TALK TO THE CAPTAINS BEFORE A GAME, BUT I WOULD BE REMISS IF I DIDN'T TAKE A MOMENT TO ADDRESS THE INCREDIBLE MOMENT WE ARE WITNESSING HERE TODAY.

THIS IS THE FIRST GAME BETWEEN THESE TWO TEAMS, AND THE FIRST GAME EVER IN THIS NEW LEAGUE. YOU ARE MAKING HISTORY TODAY, ALL OF YOU.

IT IS AN HONOR TO OFFICIATE THIS GAME.

ALL RIGHT, LET'S HAVE FUN OUT THERE.

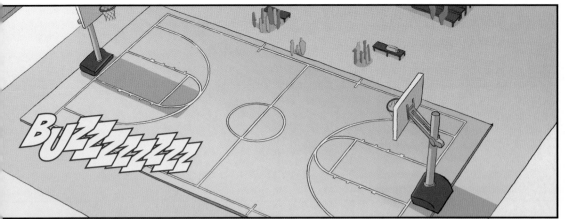

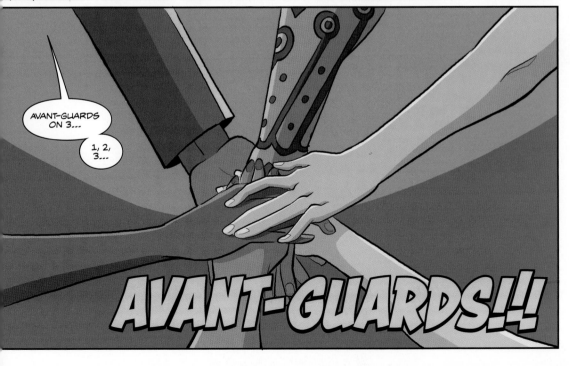

TWEEEEET

OMG OMG OMG OMG OMG

SWISH

WAIT... ARE WE...

ARE WE GOOD?!

I WAS HONESTLY NOT EXPECTING THAT.

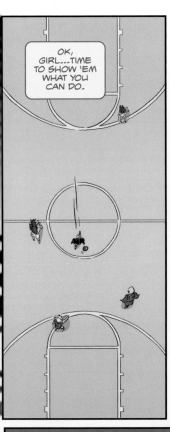

ALL OF THESE ANIMALS ARE UP FOR ADOPTION! IF YOU'RE INTERESTED, WE'LL HAVE APPLICATION FORMS IN THE LOBBY AFTER THE GAME!

ADOPT US!

WAIT, WHERE'S JAY?

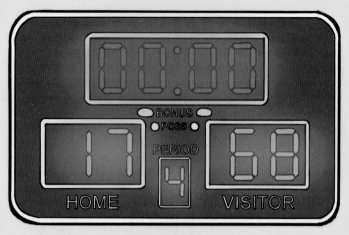

COME ON
COME ON
COME ON
COME ON...

RING
RING

DAMMIT!

HI-SCORE
65,481,190

FWIP FWIP
FWIP

OLIVIA BATES,
YOU'RE ON A HOT
STREAK.

TIME TO MAKE
YOUR MOVE.

PUNK

KISS

THERE SHE IS.

WAIT, WHO IS THAT?!

WHO IS NICOLE TALKING TO?!

UGH, SHE'S ALL OVER HIM!

GET A ROOM, YOU TWO.

÷SIGH÷ OLIVIA BATES, YOU'RE DOING IT AGAIN.

YOU'RE BETTER AS FRIENDS.

BESIDES... CHARLIE'S HERE. OH, OF *COURSE* SHE'S PLAYING POOL.

YOU'RE *KIND* OF A STEREO-TYPE.

DEATH FIGHT

PUNK

KISS

EXCUSE ME?

LEATHER JACKET *AND* POOL? ALMOST *TOO* GAY. LIKE... SUSPICIOUSLY GAY.

SCRITCH

IT'S ONLY A STEREOTYPE IF YOU'RE GOOD, WHICH I'M NOT.

SOMETIMES I THINK IT'D BE FUN TO LEARN...

BUT NOT TODAY.

COOL PARTY.

IT'S OK, NOT MY BEST WORK. BUT I DIDN'T HAVE MUCH NOTICE.

DIDN'T THINK WE'D WIN?

DIDN'T WANT TO GET MY HOPES UP...

THAT DOESN'T SEEM LIKE YOU.

THIS TEAM DIDN'T *EXIST* LAST WEEK! I'M HOPEFUL, BUT I'M NOT NAIVE.

IS IT EVERYTHING YOU THOUGHT IT WOULD BE?

THAT'S TOUGH, I'M SORRY.

THANKS, CHARLIE. YOU'RE A GOOD LISTENER.

WELL, FOR WHAT IT'S WORTH, I LOVE THAT SONG.

I WENT THROUGH A PRETTY ROUGH BREAKUP LAST YEAR.

I WAS SO INTO HER...

BUT SHE SAID SHE COULDN'T DATE A SCORPIO SUN WITH A CAPRICORN MOON...

WHATEVER THAT MEANS.

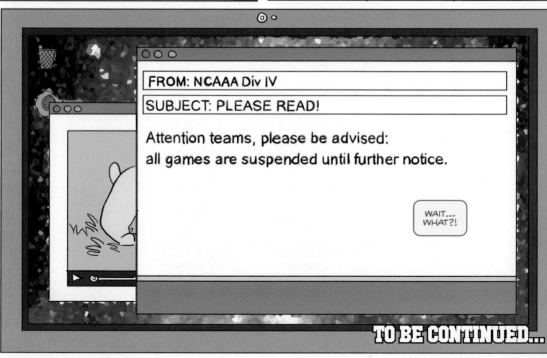

DISCOVER
ALL THE HITS

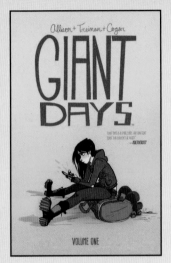

Lumberjanes
Noelle Stevenson, Shannon Watters, Grace Ellis, Brooklyn Allen, and Others
Volume 1: Beware the Kitten Holy
ISBN: 978-1-60886-687-8 | $14.99 US
Volume 2: Friendship to the Max
ISBN: 978-1-60886-737-0 | $14.99 US
Volume 3: A Terrible Plan
ISBN: 978-1-60886-803-2 | $14.99 US
Volume 4: Out of Time
ISBN: 978-1-60886-860-5 | $14.99 US
Volume 5: Band Together
ISBN: 978-1-60886-919-0 | $14.99 US

Giant Days
John Allison, Lissa Treiman, Max Sarin
Volume 1
ISBN: 978-1-60886-789-9 | $9.99 US
Volume 2
ISBN: 978-1-60886-804-9 | $14.99 US
Volume 3
ISBN: 978-1-60886-851-3 | $14.99 US

Jonesy
Sam Humphries, Caitlin Rose Boyle
Volume 1
ISBN: 978-1-60886-883-4 | $9.99 US
Volume 2
ISBN: 978-1-60886-999-2 | $14.99 US

Slam!
Pamela Ribon, Veronica Fish, Brittany Peer
Volume 1
ISBN: 978-1-68415-004-5 | $14.99 US

Goldie Vance
Hope Larson, Brittney Williams
Volume 1
ISBN: 978-1-60886-898-8 | $9.99 US
Volume 2
ISBN: 978-1-60886-974-9 | $14.99 US

The Backstagers
James Tynion IV, Rian Sygh
Volume 1
ISBN: 978-1-60886-993-0 | $14.99 US

Tyson Hesse's Diesel: Ignition
Tyson Hesse
ISBN: 978-1-60886-907-7 | $14.99 US

Coady & The Creepies
Liz Prince, Amanda Kirk, Hannah Fisher
ISBN: 978-1-68415-029-8 | $14.99 US

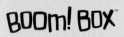

AVAILABLE AT YOUR LOCAL COMICS SHOP AND BOOKSTORE
To find a comics shop in your area, visit www.comicshoplocator.com
WWW.BOOM-STUDIOS.COM